SERIES 2
THE COMPLE
ORGAN PLAY
SONGBOO
VOLUME 1

Arranged by Kenneth Baker

G000124120

Contents

Songs

Wise Publications
London/New York/Sydney/Cologne

Exclusive Distributors:
Music Sales Limited
8/9 Frith Street, London W1V 5TZ, England.
Music Sales Pty. Limited
120 Rothschild Avenue, Rosebery, NSW 2018, Australia.

This book © Copyright 1983 by
Wise Publications
UK ISBN 0.7119.0360.3
UK Order No. AM 33721

Music Sales' complete catalogue lists thousands of titles
and is free from your local music shop, or direct from
Music Sales Limited. Please send a cheque/postal order
for £1.50 for postage to Music Sales Limited, Newmarket Road,
Bury St. Edmunds, Suffolk IP33 3YB.

Printed in Great Britain
J.B. Offset (Marks Tey) Limited, Marks Tey, Essex.

REGISTRATION TABLE
(For All Organs)

GENERAL ELECTRONIC ORGANS

(1) Upper: Flutes 8', 4'
    Lower: String 8'
    Pedal: 8'
    Vibrato: On (or Leslie: Tremolo)

(2) Upper (or Synthesizer): Clarinet 8'
    Lower: Flutes 8', 4'
    Pedal: 8'
    Vibrato: Off (Upper)
    On (Lower)

(3) Upper: Flutes 16', 8', 2', Piano

    Lower: Flute 8', String 8'
    Pedal: 8'
    Vibrato: On (or Leslie: Tremolo)

(4) Upper (or Synthesizer): Violin
    Lower: Flute 8'
    Pedal: 8'
    Vibrato: On

(5) Upper: Off. Synthesizer:
    Flute, or Pan Flute
    Lower: Orchestral Strings
    Pedal: 8'
    Vibrato: On (with Flute)
    Off (with Strings)

(6) Upper: Off. Synthesizer:
    Trombone
    Lower: Orchestral Strings
    Pedal: 8'
    Vibrato: On (with Trombone)
    Off (with Strings)

(7) Upper: Flutes 16', 8', 4'
    + Synthesizer: Saxophone
    Lower: Flutes 8', 4', String 8'
    Pedal: 16' + 8'
    Vibrato: On (or Leslie: Tremolo)

(8) Upper: Orchestral Strings +
    Synthesizer: Guitar
    Lower: Flutes 8', 4'
    Pedal: 16' + 8'
    Vibrato: Off (Upper)
    On (Lower)

DRAWBAR ORGANS

(1) Upper: 00 7600 000
    Lower: (00)4333 222(0)
    Pedal: 4 – (2)
    Vibrato: On (or Leslie: Tremolo)

(2) Upper: 00 7272 420
    Lower: (00)7503 000(0)
    Pedal: 4 – (2)
    Vibrato: Off (Upper)
    On (Lower)

(3) Upper: 80 8006 008
    + Piano
    Lower: (00)6544 333(0)
    Pedal: 5 – (3)
    Vibrato: On (or Leslie: Tremolo)

(4) Upper: 00 5666 654
    Lower: (00)6505 000(0)
    Pedal: 4 – (2)
    Vibrato: On

(5) Upper: 00 8600 000

    Lower: (00)5333 221(0)
    Pedal: 4 – (2)
    Vibrato: On (or Leslie: Tremolo)

(6) Upper: 80 5670 400

    Lower: (00)6444 222(0)
    Pedal: 5 – (3)
    Vibrato: On (or Leslie: Tremolo)

(7) Upper: 80 8683 500

    Lower: (00)8633 442(0)
    Pedal: 6 – (4)
    Vibrato: On (or Leslie: Tremolo)

(8) Upper: 00 5666 654
    + 3rd Harmonic
    Lower: (00)7504 000(0)
    Pedal: 4 – (2)
    Vibrato: On (or Leslie: Tremolo)

White Rose Of Athens

Music: Manos Hadjidakis. Words: Norman Newell. Additional Words: Archie Bleyer.

Registration No ⑤
Suggested Drum Rhythm: **Rhumba**

Banks Of The Ohio

Traditional. Arranged by Kenneth Baker

Registration No ②
Suggested Drum Rhythm: **Swing**

Puff (The Magic Dragon)

Words & Music: Peter Yarrow and Leonard Lipton

Registration No ⑦
Suggested Drum Rhythm: **Swing**

And I Love Her

Words & Music: John Lennon and Paul McCartney

Registration No ⑧
Suggested Drum Rhythm: **Bossa Nova**

Edelweiss

Words: Oscar Hammerstein II. Music: Richard Rodgers

Registration No ①
Suggested Drum Rhythm: **Waltz**

Skye Boat Song

Traditional arranged Kenneth Baker

Registration No ④
Suggested Drum Rhythm: **Waltz**

11

Be My Love

Words: Sammy Cahn. Music: Nicholas Brodszky

Registration No ②
Suggested Drum Rhythm: **Swing**

Be my love, for no one else can end this yearn - ing, This need that you and you a - lone cre - ate. Just fill my arms the way you've filled my dreams The dreams that you in - spire with ev - 'ry sweet de - sire

*i.e. Eb⁰

That Lucky Old Sun

Words: Haven Gillespie. Music: Beasley Smith

Registration No ⑥
Suggested Drum Rhythm: **Bossa Nova**

(Is This The Way To) Amarillo

Words & Music: Neil Sedaka & Howard Greenfield

Registration No ①
Suggested Drum Rhythm: **Rock**

*i.e. Ab7, omitting note G

It Happened In Monterey

Words: Billy Rose. Music: Mabel Wayne

Registration No ②
Suggested Drum Rhythm: **Waltz**

Love's Been Good To Me

Words & Music: Rod McKuen

Registration No ④
Suggested Drum Rhythm: **Bossa Nova**

A Certain Smile

Words: Paul Francis Webster. Music: Sammy Fain

Registration No ①
Suggested Drum Rhythm: **Swing**

* A new high inversion, more convenient here
** Usual inversion

Ramona

Lyric: L Wolfe Gilbert. Music: Mabel Wayne

Registration No ④
Suggested Drum Rhythm: **Waltz**

mem-ber the ram-bling rose you wear in your hair. Ra-

mon-a, when day is done you'll hear my call___ Ra-

mon-a, we'll meet be-side the wa-ter-fall___ I

dread the dawn when I a-wake to find you gone, Ra-

mon-a, I need you my own.

When I Grow Too Old To Dream

Words: Oscar Hammerstein II. Music: Sigmund Romberg

Registration No ⑥
Suggested Drum Rhythm: **Waltz**

The Surrey With The Fringe On Top

Words: Oscar Hammerstein II. Music: Richard Rodgers

Registration No ③
Suggested Drum Rhythm: **Swing**

The Green Leaves Of Summer

Words: Paul Francis Webster. Music: Dimitri Tiomkin.

Registration No ⑤
Suggested Drum Rhythm: **Waltz**

Help

Words & Music: John Lennon and Paul McCartney

Registration No ⑧
Suggested Drum Rhythm: **Rock**

* i.e. E♭7, omitting note "D♭"

Be-Bop-A-Lula

Words & Music: Gene Vincent and Sheriff Tex Davis

Registration No ⑦
Suggested Drum Rhythm: **Swing**

VERSE

She's the girl in the red blue jeans, She's the queen of all the teens, She's the one ____ that I know. She's the one that loves me so.

CHORUS

Be-bop-a-lu-la, She's my ba-by, Be-bop-a-lu-la, I don't mean may-be, Be-bop-a-lu-la, She's my ba-by love, my ba-by love, my ba-by love.

I Will Survive

Words & Music: Dino Fekaris & Freddie Perren

Registration No ⑤
Suggested Drum Rhythm: **Rock**

*i.e. Am7, omitting note "G"

The Wonder Of You

Words & Music: Baker Knight

Registration No ⑥
Suggested Drum Rhythm: **Swing**

Singin' In The Rain

Words: Arthur Freed. Music: Nacio Herb Brown

Registration No ③
Suggested Drum Rhythm: **Swing**

Hello Goodbye

Words & Music: John Lennon & Paul McCartney

Registration No ⑦
Suggested Drum Rhythm: **Rock**

Money, Money, Money

Words & Music: Benny Andersson and Bjorn Ulvaeus

Registration No ③
Suggested Drum Rhythm: **Rock**

fool a - round and have a ball.

CHORUS

Mo - ney, mo - ney, mo - ney, must be fun - ny In the rich man's world

Mo - ney, mo - ney, mo - ney, al - ways sun - ny In the rich man's world, A -

ha _____ a - ha All the things I could do If I

had a lit - tle mo - ney, It's a rich man's world.

With A Little Help From My Friends

Words & Music: John Lennon and Paul McCartney

Registration No ⑧
Suggested Drum Rhythm: **Swing**

♩ = 100

Upper

Lower

Pedal

What would you do _ if I sang _ out of tune _ would you stand

_ up and walk _ out on me? _ Lend me your ears _ and I'll sing

_ you a song _ and I'll try _ not to sing _ out of key. _ Oh I get by _

_ with a little help from my friends _ Mm, I get high.

CHORD CHART (For Left Hand)

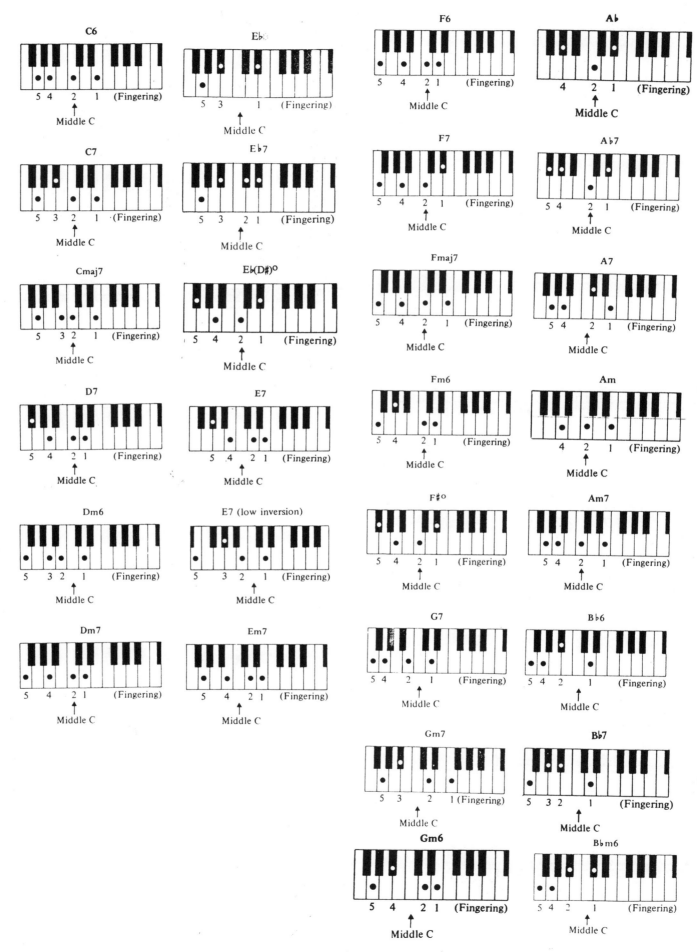